Dear Family and Friends of Young Readers,

Learning to read is one of the most important milestones your child will ever attain. Early reading is hard work, but you can make it easier with Hello Readers.

Just like learning to play a sport or an instrument, learning to read requires many opportunities to work on skills. However, you have to get in the game or experience real music to keep interested and motivated. Hello Readers are carefully structured to provide the right level of text for practice and great stories for experiencing the fun of reading.

Try these activities:

• Reading starts with the alphabet and at the earliest level, you may encourage your child to focus on the sounds of letters in words and sounding out words. With more experienced readers, focus on how words are spelled. Be word watchers!

• Go beyond the book—talk about the story, how it compares with other stories, and what your child likes about it.

• Comprehension—did your child get it? Have your child retell the story or answer questions you may ask about it.

Another thing children learn to do at this age is learn to ride a bike. You put training wheels on to help them in the beginning and guide the bike from behind. Hello Readers help you support your child and then you get to watch them take off as skilled readers.

—Francie Al
Chief Acac
Scholastic

crow

For Justin and Kate

— M.P.

For Aron

— E.K.

Go to *www.scholastic.com* for website information on
Scholastic authors and illustrators.

Library of Congress Cataloging-in-Publication-Data available.

12 11 10 9 8 7 6 5 4 3 2 1   2 3 4 5 6 7/0

Printed in the U.S.A.
First printing, September 2002

by Mary Packard
Illustrated by Eleanor Kwei

Hello Reader! — Level 1

SCHOLASTIC INC.

New York   Toronto   London   Auckland   Sydney
Mexico City   New Delhi   Hong Kong   Buenos Aires

"Time to get up,"
the farmer said.
"You can't scare crows
while you're still in bed."

Oh, *no,* thought Rags,
I don't want to go.
I'm much too shy
to scare a crow.

Like all straw children
everywhere,
Rags had to learn
the right way to scare.

Since crows are smart
and hard to fool,
straw children go
to scarecrow school.

Rags liked to count
and to add and subtract.
He wanted to learn
each and every new fact.

Like how to tell
a crow from a jay—
and ways to make
them fly away.

Rags learned to tell time
by watching the sun.
And reading cloud pictures
was always such fun.

He watched as his friends
learned to make scary faces
and stuff straw in their clothes
in all the right places.

But when it came time
for Scare and Tell,
poor Rags did his best,
but he didn't do well!

"Rags," said his teacher,
"please don't despair.
Each scarecrow must find
his own way to scare."

So Rags kept his chin up.
He tried not to mope.
He worked very hard.
He did not give up hope.

In art class, Rags usually
made bright, cheery things.
But this time he made
a blue monster with wings.

It had a big beak
and bright, shiny scales,
a tinfoil tail,
and sharp, scary nails.

As Rags walked home
through fields of corn rows,
he heard a flock
of rude, noisy crows.

They swooped and chattered.
They were having a race.
Rags used his blue monster
to cover his face.

"Caw, caw!" cried the crows.
"You can't scare us!"
Then they saw the blue beast,
and that started a fuss.

In a minute, the crows
had flown off in a fright.
Rags looked around.
Not one was in sight.

Rags laughed out loud,
and he started to run.
"Who knew scaring crows
could be so much fun!"